ETYMOLOGY
for wordbrains like me

written by
Norm Bomer
illustrated by
Rich Bishop

Wordbrain Paperbacks
GWP, INC. • *Asheville, North Carolina*

First Edition, 2007
Published in the United States of America by
Wordbrain Paperbacks
85 Tunnel Road, Suite 12
Asheville, NC 28803

10 9 8 7 6 5 4 3 2 1

Text Copyright © 2007 Norm Bomer
Illustrations Copyright © 2007 Rich Bishop
Some material contained in this book was previously published in *Top Story*.

Published in paperback in the United States of America by Wordbrain Paperbacks, a division of GWP, Inc., Asheville, North Carolina.

ISBN 0-9779299-3-0

Cover design by Trudy Wells
Book design and layout by Matthew Mulder and Trudy Wells

TABLE OF CONTENTS

ETYMOLOGY

Forget the "n." Don't even think about it. This word is long enough without it.

There. I've said it. And you have no idea why.

My name, by the way, is Professor Wordbrain. Want to know the origin and history of a word? Want to know what it used to mean and what it means now? Want to know if there's any weird stuff going on?

I have answers.

You, of course, see the word "etymology" on this page and on the cover. It is long enough to scare even people with brains larger than mine (if such people exist). Fear not.

Big words are often like big, friendly dogs: monsters on the outside, puppies on the inside.

Now, about that mysterious "n." There is a word that looks like "etymology" with an "n" crammed into it. That word, "entomology," means "the study of insects." That is NOT what we are talking about today. Don't even think about it.

Our word "etymology" (no "n," no insects) comes from the ancient Greek word *etymon*. It meant "true meaning." The "-logy" part of "etymology" comes from the Greek word *logos*. It meant "word."

There you have it. "Etymology" means "the true meaning of words" or "the study of words."

So when talking to your friends about my book, just casually throw in the word "etymology" as if it's as common to you as "toast" or "love."

After all, it only looks scary. Its meaning is sweet and simple. And being a wordbrain (small "w"), you just happen to know precisely what it is.

BUTTERFLY

Do you think of butterflies only in the spring and summer? I like to think about them in the dead of winter myself. Where I live we could use a few butterflies about then.

But whether you see the little darlins fluttering about your yard or see only snow and ice out there, you may wonder where that word "butterfly" comes from. Is it just a cute way of saying "flutter by" without saying "flutter by"?

After all, almost every butterfly I've ever met fluttered by. But no. That has absolutely nothing to do with it.

Now what? Well, let's move from entomology to etymology. This word "butterfly" is so old (way over a thousand years) that no one knows for sure. But some folks that are really smart are almost sure they almost know for sure.

Here it is: So many—maybe most—butterflies are yellow or sort-of-yellow. Like butter, you know. The word "butterfly" started long ago in Europe. And the most common butterfly there was the yellow sulfur.

Okay, let me get this straight. Butterflies look like butter that flies by? So why don't horseflies look like horses?

PERSPICACIOUS

Do you know anyone with a mouth long enough to speak a word as long as this one? Or does it require only a really long brain and an average mouth?

Well, the good news is that you are at this very moment hearing from a genuine Wordbrain who happens to have a wordbrain just long enough for this occasion. As for my mouth, well, I won't bore you about that.

"Perspicacious," even if you can't say it without practicing for two hours and ten minutes like I did, has a rather plain meaning. But that is not to say perspicacious people are plain people. I suspect you yourself are quite perspicacious and not quite plain.

The word comes, as so many English words do, from the ancient Latin. *Per* meant "through" and *spicere* meant "to look" or "to see." So if you are a perspicacious person, you are someone who can see through things—and I am not referring to windows or air.

I'm talking about seeing through people—as in figuring

out what they are thinking but not admitting. I'm talking about having uncommon insight and discernment. I'm talking about being sharp as a tack.

Since you are reading this book, you are undoubtedly almost as perspicacious as this modest Professor with the longish brain. There are few people who are able to pull the wool over your eyes. You can see right through their not-so-clever attempts to make you think they are geniuses just because they can say "perspicacious" right straight through without gulping for air.

EAT CROW

There may be a long list of things people would like to do to crows. Eating is not one of them.

Crows, as you might have noticed, are annoying, croaky, loud, messy, pushy, and rather large birds that love to peck dead things. You may at times feel like shooing them away—or adding a "t" and shooting them. But—and this is one of those annoying things—they don't really care what you feel like. They're brassy, bold, brave, and just all-around disrespectful.

To make matters worse, they are smart. Although they obviously don't care what you think, they seem to know what you think. Is that annoying or what?

If you are with me so far, you're probably ready to bite the head off the nearest crow. Don't try it. For one thing, you probably cannot outsmart the nearest crow long enough to catch it. For another, you would not want to bite its head—or any other part of it.

Crow meat is nothing like the meat of doves, ducks,

or chickens. Crow meat is several notches worse than roach meat.

There is an old saying that if you're lost and starving, just shoot a crow and boil it with one of your boots for a long time. Then eat the boot.

You have probably gotten the hint that eating crow is not a delightful pastime. To eat crow would be awful and humiliating.

That's why when you hear someone say he had to eat crow, he's saying he had to admit he was wrong and humble himself in front of everyone. As humiliating as that can be, it's sometimes exactly the right thing to do.

No one can say that about eating the real thing.

TOWHEAD

Were you ever one of those? A towhead?

Maybe you heard someone call you that. Maybe it was even someone who loves you. Maybe you felt a bit self-conscious. Maybe you wondered if your head looked like a big toe.

Well, maybe it did. I think mine did.

But fear not. A towhead is not the same as a toehead. That's because "tow" is not "toe."

The word "tow" goes back more than a thousand years to an Old English word of the same spelling. It was and still is the word for the raw fibers of plants like hemp and flax, used for weaving. Before being woven, such fibers are scruffy and light-colored.

So if your head was ever covered with rather scruffy, light-colored hair, you were a towhead, plain and simple. That was true even if no one ever said so. No offense intended.

And if your head does happen to look like a big toe, maybe you'd better wear a stocking cap.

LIKE

Back in the good 'ol days, "like" meant something like (similar to) love (super liking). But these days, "like" isn't used to mean either "similar to" or "love" nearly as much as it is used to mean . . . .

And that's, like, where we run into, like, problems. You see, the new and more popular use of "like" has, like, no meaning. It's like (similar to) "uh" or "um" and is generally used when the head, like, suddenly goes, like, empty. And who likes that?

Well, like, lots of people do. You may think they're, like, mostly teenage girls from, like, Southern California. But no. It's, like, boys too—and even, like, lots of men and women. And from, like, all over.

Actually this, like, new use of "like" isn't so new. Back in the 1950s, there was an odd little cultural group known as the Beatniks. They, like, wore black turtlenecks and goatees (mostly, like, guys wore those). And they, like, sat around burning candles, beating bongo drums, and reading depressing poems in, like, Greenwich Village, New York.

They also, like, said things like (such as) "like, cool, man" and "like, crazy, Daddy-o."

I must admit, there is at least one, like, use of the word these days that has, like, some meaning. The word is sometimes used instead of "said." So I guess that is, like, what it means sometimes.

Like, "My dad's like, 'Why do you talk like that?'"

KIDNAP

Sometimes you could be better off not thinking about what you're saying.

Oops. Parents would not want me saying such a thing if their kids are listening. I'd better explain.

I did not mean you should just let your lips flap without using good sense. I meant that thinking about certain common words can get really confusing. If you think about them, they just don't make sense.

Unless, of course, you have Professor Wordbrain to put your troubled mind at ease.

Take "kidnap," for example. It makes no sense. I mean, usually it's not kids that are napped. It's grownups. And besides, what's "napped"? Sounds like they just finished an afternoon snooze. And we all know that people held for ransom have trouble sleeping.

Well, here's the sense of it: "Kidnapped" was a slang word invented in 1600s England. "Kid" did mean "child" back then. And "nap" was just a form of "nab," meaning to grab or to steal. The word referred to the popular but nasty practice of snatching young boys to work on ships and in British colonies.

So if you're a kid who takes naps, I hope you don't lose any sleep over words that don't necessarily mean what they look like.

KNOT

Okay, slow down. You're already moving too fast.

You're not? You're knot?

Your not? I didn't know you had one. If you do, how fast is it? And who tied it?

Now that I have slowed you down into utter confusion, just leave it to me—the clever and resourceful Professor Wordbrain—to make things crystal clear. Well, for the sake of honesty, let's say glass clear. Tinted glass maybe?

Long ago on the high seas, before the days of speedometers and GPS units and radar, seafarers had a clever and resourceful way of measuring their speed. Actually, they called it logging their speed. They used real logs too.

They tied a very long string to a log. They tied a bunch of evenly-spaced knots in the string—one every 47 feet. Then they tossed the log into the water.

As the ship went forward, the string played out behind. As it did, the sailors counted how many knots slipped out the back of the ship in 28 seconds.

One knot meant they were traveling at one nautical mile per hour. Ten knots meant they were traveling at ten nautical miles per hour—a speed of ten knots. Pretty simple, huh?

Why 28 seconds and why 47 feet? Well, 28 seconds is a small fraction of an hour. And 47 feet is the same small fraction of a nautical mile.

Sailors could have spaced their knots one mile apart

and counted how many went by in an hour. But can you imagine how much string and how much time that would take to calculate speed?

Seafarers today don't log their speed like that anymore. But they still use the word "knot" to mean one nautical mile per hour.

And if that's not tinted-glass clear or better, I am KNOT responsible.

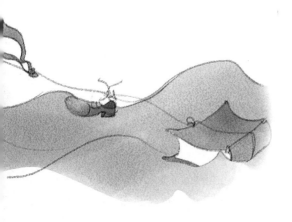

UNDERDOG

It's quite simple, really—just as it was quite simple back in the 1870s. That's when dog fighting was a legal and popular sport in America. Popular, that is, with humans. Not so popular with dogs.

Let me re-phrase that.

Not so popular with underdogs. The top dogs were okay with it.

You may be catching on to the quite simple meaning of "underdog." Two dogs have at it. One dog wins. The other dog loses. How do you know which is which at the end of the fight? Of course. The winning dog is on top. So it's the top dog. I don't know why no one called it the overdog.

The underdog is under a soft quilt having a little snooze. Oops. Professor Wordbrain never speaks a lie. He just kids around a little bit.

No, actually the losing pooch is flat on its back under the winner. It still has its teeth bared and still looks tough, but that's all an act at this point. The underdog is the loser. Period.

Now, these days we continue to use that word "underdog," but not so much for dogs and not even so much for definite losers. These days, we use the word to mean something more like "likely loser" or "come-from-behind contender" or "the team that no one expects has much of a chance to win anything and probably won't, even though it would be pretty cool if it surprised everybody and beat the socks off that uppity team with all the power and money."

And speaking of Sox, . . . Oops, sorry. Some top dog just Yanked my pen away.

CAR

The Normans invaded England in 1066, and their leader, William the Conqueror, became king of England. The Normans spoke their own brand of French, so it became the common language of England's ruling class. That means the English language was French.

I don't mean to confuse you, but that's history. The Normans eventually mixed with England's Anglo-Saxons, and, of course, their languages mixed too. Our modern English developed from that.

So did cars.

What? Well, okay, not exactly. But the word "car" does have deep roots in the old Norman French language. That's why I told you all that stuff. Those Normans drove cars way back then. They were actually chariots, but their word for chariot was *carre*. Yes, ancient peoples and later the Romans were not the only ones who drove chariots.

Speaking of those Romans, you probably remember that their language was Latin. You probably remember too that lots of words in later languages were based on old Latin words. The Norman French *carre* was one of those. It came from the Latin word *carrus* which meant "cart" or "wagon."

Now you know where we English speakers got the word "car." It's really just a short form of "carriage"—related to "carry."

By the way, you may be wondering how the word "automobile" fits into all this. Well, in our modern language, a car and an automobile are the same thing. But "automobile" is a much newer word. It didn't start until the mid-1890s, when people started making horseless carriages, first with steam engines and then with gasoline engines.

"Auto" means "self." "Mobile" means "moving." An automobile is a vehicle that moves itself and doesn't need horses to pull it or people to push it.

Unless, of course, it's a . . . . Well, I guess I shouldn't mention the brand of car that breaks down all the time. But if you ever see one sitting beside the road, please stop and offer a push.

SOMBRERO

Hold on to your hats, vaqueros! We're going on a word ride!

Did I say hats? I meant sombreros. After all, the Spanish word *vaquero* means "cowboy." And vaqueros don't wear hats. They wear sombreros.

You know a sombrero when you see one. It's more than a regular cowboy hat. It's like an umbrella hat, if you could call it that. And you could.

You could also call it a shade hat. Like an umbrella, it provides plenty of shade for a vaquero or anyone else with a head beneath it. And that's a sober thought.

Sober? What's sober about a sombrero? Perhaps I should have said "somber," because that word means "dark and gloomy."

"Somber" goes way back to 1760 and the old French word *sombre* with the same dark meaning. And *sombre* goes way, way back to the ancient Latin word *subumbrare*, meaning "to shade" or "to shadow."

All those gloomy ideas certainly aren't sunny. Look closely at the spelling of that ancient Latin word. Do you see the makings of "umbrella" hidden there in the shade?

Now look at the spellings of all these dark old words. Do they remind you of "sombrero"? They should. For "sombrero" comes from some of those same French and Latin words. After all, a "sombrero" does provide shade—

just like an umbrella. In fact, long ago, "sombrero" actually meant "umbrella." It came from an old Spanish word *sombra*, meaning "shade."

Does that mean a bright and happy vaquero will get somber and gloomy when he puts on a sombrero? Not at all. In fact, if it's a really hot and sunny day, he will be quite happy in its cool shade.

TWEAK

The engine in your race car is running just a little rough. So you figure you'd better tweak it a bit before the green flag starts waving.

Or maybe you write a poem and hand it in. Your teacher says it's good but could be better. She hands it back to you for a little tweaking.

You get the idea. To tweak something is to give it a minor adjustment. That meaning has been around for only a few decades. But the word itself has been around for more like 400 years. So how was it used during its first few centuries?

Well, if you had ever been tweaked by my grandma, you would know. The original meaning of "tweak" was something like "pinch" or "give a quick twist." I think tweaking was usually done to someone's nose. Maybe it was just a little sign of affection. Or maybe it was to adjust slightly crooked noses.

In my grandma's case, it was a cheek thing. She would

pinch a good hunk of my tender face flesh between her thumb and the knuckle of her first finger. Then she'd twist it and tell me how cute I was.

I don't think I was too cute with my face scrunched up in pain and my mouth wide open in a silent scream. If tweaking was a sign of affection, I was glad my grandma didn't love me more than that.

I like the newer meaning of tweak. If you want to tweak something, pinch and twist an engine and leave my tender face alone.

POSEUR

It looks like a French word. But it's a poseur, so maybe it isn't really French. We have reason to be suspicious. Let's check it out.

Yes, it's French. But "poseur" has been adopted by the English language as well. So now it's an English word too.

In case you're wondering why I said we should be suspicious, it's because of the word itself. A poseur is someone who puts on some kind of phony act—just to make a highfalutin impression on others.

You can usually spot a poseur a mile away. But sometimes it's not so easy. Some people are pretty good actors.

The word "poseur" is directly related to the word "pose." It refers to someone who pretends to be what he isn't. He's just posing, just putting on a false front.

You may be wondering why such a person is not simply called a "poser." Why the fancy French spelling?

Well, such a person actually can be called a poser. A poseur is the same thing—except that a poseur is always the phony kind. A poser can also be someone who poses for a picture. Nothing phony about that.

So next time you dress up for a family portrait, please remember to be a poser and not a poseur. Leave the superhero cape in your closet.

LUKEWARM

I can't explain it. So please let me explain. I mean, I can explain lukewarm, but I can't explain it.

This isn't going well, is it? Time to start over.

I can explain where the word "lukewarm" comes from. It was first used about 400 years ago. "Lukewarm" came from the word "luke," which came from the older word "lew," which came from the much older word "hleow." Luke, lew, and hleow all meant the same thing: "slightly warm."

This brings me to the part I cannot explain. I have no idea why anyone 400 years ago would say "lukewarm." Wasn't luke enough by itself? Lukewarm was the same as saying warmwarm. Still is today.

That's why I'm so confused. If something is lukewarm, then it's warmwarm, which is twice as warm as warm, which is pretty hot. But lukewarm means not hot at all and barely warm.

Hey, all this hard thinking has got my motor overheated. You could say I'm warmwarm, but I wouldn't advise it.

Someone might think I'm hardly warm at all. And that would be uncool.

MOOCH

If you've been the victim of mooching, you have a certain negative appreciation for it. Mooching is annoying.

If you've been doing the mooching, you may have an altogether different type of appreciation for it. Maybe you appreciate whatever it is you've gotten away with. And you don't care how annoying you've been.

But whatever it is people appreciate, a moocher isn't included.

A moocher, of course, is someone who sponges off other people, a freeloader who always needs to "borrow" some cash at the last minute and always forgets to pay it back. A moocher is someone who leaves you alone at the table just before the waitress brings the bill.

The word "mooch" didn't show up with that meaning until the middle of the 1800s. That doesn't mean there were no moochers skulking around before that. The modern word probably goes back hundreds of years to the Middle English word *mucchen*, which meant to be stingy.

Mucchen probably came from *mucche*, which meant "nightcap." That's because of the tightwads that hid their money in their nightcaps.

There was also the Old French word *muchier*, which meant to sneak around and be just an all-around shady and stingy character.

Moochers, you know, aren't actually out of money. They've got plenty stashed away in nightcaps. They only pretend to be broke so someone else will pick up the tab.

Now, if you're thinking this word popped into my head because of you, rest at ease. It's because, well, I accidentally forgot my billfold, and I was wondering if you could spare me a couple of bucks.

MAYDAY

Not many folks observe the old May Day holiday anymore. May Day—the first day of May—used to be a time to celebrate the glories of spring. There were flower festivals and picnics. People gave "May baskets" of flowers and treats to their friends.

So why is it that people in serious trouble cry "Mayday! Mayday!"? Do you cry "Flowers! Flowers!" when you're stuck in quicksand? Do you cry "Picnic! Picnic!" when a flood carries away your pet crocodile? Of course not.

The fact is, the distress call "Mayday!" was adopted in 1927 as an official international call for help. It's somewhat like sending an SOS, but perhaps with more urgency.

If your ship has lost its way, you probably send out an SOS signal. If it's sinking, you probably cry "Mayday! Mayday!"

And all that has absolutely nothing to do with May flowers. "Mayday" is actually an English adaptation of a French word that sounds just about the same. The French word is spelled *m'aider* and means "help me!"

"Mayday" is easy to say in an emergency and easy to understand—even when heard over a distant radio full of static. So when you're enjoying your flower basket on the first of May, please don't get too excited and start yelling "May Day! May Day!"

Unless, of course, you want a U.S. Coast Guard helicopter landing on your picnic blanket.

DUMBBELL

Please be patient. I know what you're thinking. The word "dumbbell" probably describes me better than "wordbrain." But hold your judgment for just a moment—even though it may be accurate. Let me tell you where the word "dumbbell" came from originally. Then you can decide if you think I came from the same place.

Way, way back, even before I was born, people in Europe started building bell towers. When I say way, way, I mean over a thousand years ago. Tower bells would be rung for everyone in the community to hear. The bigger the bell, the bigger the sound, the farther the distance.

Some bells were so big that it took a real muscleman like me (I did not say muscle head) to pull the rope that made them swing and ring. And, believe it or not, other bells were far bigger than that. They sometimes required ten or twenty men to ring them.

Some guys actually worked out to build their bell-ringing muscles. It was common to hang a heavy weight on a practice rope for that purpose. Of course, the practice "bell" didn't ring. It was dumb, which means it could not "talk."

That's why, over the centuries, other weights used for physical training came to be called dumbbells. And when they were attached to long bars, they were called barbells.

Oh, just a sec. Yes, you there in the back row with your hand up. Do you have a question?

You say you've been patient? You've held your judgment? Do I remember something about a fitting name for me?

No, sorry. That doesn't ring a bell.

POLLYWOG

You may say "tadpole" if you want to. But those of us who are more sophisticated in the ways of mud puddles will use the term "pollywog."

Please join us. Go first class. You can wash the mud off later.

You do, of course know what a tadpole is. That word goes clear back to the Middle English language (about 800 years ago). It was made from the words *tadde*, meaning "toad," and *pol*, meaning "head."

The word *taddepol* meant simply "toad head." The idea was that a tadpole is a toad that has almost nothing but a head in its larva stage. Of course, a tadpole does have a wiggly tail too. But it is mostly head.

The word "tadpole," by the way, is also used for a frog larva. You really can't tell which is which until it becomes an adult or you somehow get it to confess sooner. Anyway, why am I spending so much time on this inferior word? I guess it's just to tune you up for the great "pollywog."

Like "tadpole," this word also comes from Middle English. The Middle English word *polwygle* came from that same word for "head" (*pol*) and from *wiglen*, which meant "wiggle." Instead of "toad head," *polwygle* meant "wiggle head." You can see why.

All that is good news. That's because you can use the word "pollywog" for either a toad larva or a frog larva, since they are both wiggle heads. Not only is it more accurate, it's safer. You do not have to force a confession just to find out if you're dealing with a toad head or a frog head.

GUMSHOE

You recognize a compound word when you see it. It is simply a word made by sticking two or more smaller words together—like "newspaper" or "businessman" or "spitball." Guess what you're looking at right there at the head of this story. Yes, a genuine and rather quiet American compound word.

I'll tell you about the quiet part in a moment. But first, let me ask you a gum question. That's a "g," by the way.

What do you imagine to be the meaning of this word? Probably, you may be thinking, it has to do with stepping in something icky and having to scrape it off the sole of your shoe with a stick or a putty knife.

Good guess. Not accurate, however. The word actually means "detective"—usually "private detective." It's not used much anymore. But it was pretty popular back in the 1900s. It was actually invented just after the turn of that century.

These days, athletic sneakers (often called tennis shoes even when they never touch a tennis court) are very common for healthy lifestyles. So are other types of soft-soled shoes.

A hundred years ago, however, shoes like those were a fairly new thing. People referred to the soft, rubbery material in the soft soles as "gum." But the name "gumshoe," oddly enough, wasn't used for the gum-soled shoes themselves. It came to refer to detectives.

Of course, lots of people wore gum-soled shoes. But the idea of sneaking around with quiet shoes was reserved for those few professional snoopers who were more concerned about being stealthy than about being healthy.

CHUBBY

Have you ever heard of a sharky baby or a trouty baby or a carpy baby? I haven't either. But why?

That's a question that often comes up in the study of word origins. Sometimes it has no satisfying explanation.

Take the word "chubby" for example. Everyone knows what it means. And where it comes from is pretty easy to explain. It comes from the word "chub."

But why?

A chub is a thick, stubby little fish often used for bait in ocean fishing. So you might figure that being chubby means being like a chub which means being a bit thick and stubby. And if you happen to figure it that way, you will be right.

However, I'm afraid I cannot tell you why. If you could go back 400 years and talk to the first people who called babies "chubby," perhaps they could explain it. And you could ask them why they didn't call fat babies cowy or loafy or pumpkiny or walrussy or blimpy instead.

(Don't say it. I know they didn't have blimps back then. But if you could go back 400 years, surely you could tell them about blimps while you're there.)

For a sweet little baby, couldn't those folks have come up with a better metaphor than a stinky little fish? Come to think of it, perhaps the "thick and stubby" aspect of a chub wasn't on their minds at all.

BRAND-NEW

This is a hot topic. And it's a brand-new one for a Professor Wordbrain study. Isn't that cool?

Don't answer that.

The reason I call "brand-new" a hot topic is simple. It comes from the fire. The "brand" part goes back about 1500 years to the Old English language. It simply meant "a piece of burning wood." It was also referred to as a "firebrand." Those meanings are the same today.

The term "brand-new" simply means "fresh out of the fire" or "just made" or "entirely new"—like a freshly-made iron horseshoe that's still glowing red from the blacksmith's fire.

Perhaps you have noticed something a little odd about the way people say "brand-new" these days. They leave out the "d." You probably do the same thing. We all say "bran-new," even though it isn't really spelled that way.

That's because some folks have spelled it that way and even do spell it that way—even though it's not completely accurate. Authors such as Charles Dickens and Mark Twain, for example, spelled it "bran-new" in their books.

The great William Shakespeare had his own way to write it: "fire-new."

But however you say it or spell it, the meaning is the same. Something brand-new is, well, like something hot out of the oven. And that reminds me, it's time for lunch.

See ya.

ARKANSAS

And you always thought it was proper to say "Arkansaw." Well, maybe for you it was. But not for me.

You see, I used to live in the wonderful, spectacular, friendly, gorgeous, homey, and lovely state of Kansas. And no one in Kansas says "Kansaw." It's pretty obvious why.

I mean, do you call a canvas a "canvaw"? Well, maybe if you're from Arkansaw.

To be honest with you, people from Arkansas do have good reason to mispronounce their state. It started with the French. You see, French explorer La Salle declared the place a French territory in 1682. For 80 years, France claimed it.

Of course, the Ugakhapah (also called Quapaw) Indians had claimed it long before that. The French couldn't easily say "Ugakhapah" Indians, so for some reason they figured "Arkansa" Indians sounded close enough. They created the word "Arkansas" by adding an "s" for plural.

The French named the main river the River of the Arkansas (the River of the Arkansa Indians).

English-speaking Americans made Arkansas a U.S. territory in 1819. Using the old French pronunciation, they officially spelled it "Arkansaw." But the French spelling eventually came back and replaced that.

By the way, if you think the names Arkansas and Kansas are related, it's easy to see why. But strangely enough, they are not—even though the two states are next-door neighbors. Kansas got its name from the Kansa Indians—no relation to the Quapaws.

In Arkansas today, the Arkansas River is pronounced "Arkansaw" River. But that same river flows through the wonderful, spectacular, etc., state of Kansas. People there speak English. It is called the ArKANSAS River.

LOUSY

It's tough to explain the meaning of "lousy" on such a beautiful day. Nothing seems lousy to me, except that the countryside is lousy with folks enjoying God's colorful creation.

And how can that be lousy?

You may have noticed a strange little twist in the meaning of "lousy" in what I just said. First, I used the word to mean something like "disgusting" or "really bad." That's why I said nothing seems lousy to me today. There's nothing disgusting or really bad about a perfectly gorgeous day.

The disgusting sense of "lousy" goes back at least a thousand years to the Old English word "louse." And if you've ever met a louse, you know just how disgusting that is. If you've met more than one, you've met "lice," the plural of "louse."

Ask someone who has had itchy little swarms of lice playing hide-and-seek in his or her hair. To have lice is to be lousy. And that indeed is really bad.

But what about that other thing I said about the colorful countryside being lousy with people? What could be lousy about a beautiful day?

Well, this use of the word also goes back to that annoying swarm of lice. But it has nothing disgusting or really bad about it. It just means the countryside is swarming with people like a scalp swarming with lice. It does not mean the countryside is itchy and miserable. And it does not mean the people are annoying.

Well, maybe one or two of them.

ITS

Now, why would a word professor as distinguished as yours-truly waste his (and your) time on such an ITiotic little word? Well, I'll tell you.

"Its" may be little, but the list of people who don't understand it is big. I'm sure you don't ever want to appear on that list. If you ever did, I would have to take away all your apostrophe privileges for a period of one comma.

From the time you've been able to read and write, you have been taught to use an apostrophe to show possession (ownership). Nouns and pronouns that do that are, naturally, called possessive.

For example, if Bob possesses a squished banana, we say it is "Bob's" squished banana. Notice the apostrophe.

If Emily possesses an eagle feather, we do not say it is "Emily's" eagle feather—at least not too loudly. Because, believe it or not, possessing eagle feathers is now against the law. The use of that apostrophe, however, is perfectly legal and correct.

That brings us to "its." Imagine your car losing a wheel. Do you say your car lost "it's" wheel? No, I hope not. The word "it's" is a contraction and a contraction only. It means "it is."

The absolutely and wonderfully correct way to describe your car's problem is to say, without apostrophe, your car lost "its" wheel.

But that wouldn't necessarily be true, would it? You may be too young to own a car.

POTSHOT

A potshot is not a shot at a pot, although that can be fun at the target range. A pot shot is not a practice shot or a straight shot or a hot shot. A pot shot is more like a cheap shot.

Cheap shots are mean, lowdown, hurtful comments just thrown about carelessly. They don't show much responsibility. Surely you've never taken one of those at anyone. Pot shots aren't quite that mean and lowdown. But like the cheap ones, they require no real skill or knowledge.

The original term "potshot" started in America about 150 years ago. It simply meant a shot fired for the sole purpose of killing something to eat—something for the pot. A potshot was like shooting randomly into a large flock of ducks. The shooter wasn't really aiming carefully. He just figured he'd probably hit something for supper.

On the other hand, picking out one target and aiming carefully is a matter of skill. That's not a potshot.

"Potshot" has also come to mean a critical comment

just blown out there without any real skill or knowledge. As in a typical political campaign, it's sure to cause some damage to an opponent, even if it has no careful argument nor even truth behind it.

And that baffles me. Potshots can be deadly. But I don't know too many Republicans or Democrats either one who would want to cook their opponents for supper. Their tastes are far too different.

COOKIE

Forgive me for making your tummy growl and your mouth water right in the middle of your reading. I just figured you could ease my own pain a little by suffering with me.

You see, at this very moment I cannot get my mind off chocolate chip cookies—frozen ones. Yes, I am revealing to you one of my most valuable secrets: A frozen chocolate chip cookie is superior to a non-frozen one—even though my own son disagrees. Don't worry. His tastes will improve with age.

But since I am Professor Wordbrain and not Professor Foodbrain, I really should tell you where the word "cookie" comes from. The simple fact is that it comes from America and started almost exactly 300 years ago. That's when there were lots of Dutch people coming to the New World.

Every Dutch mom knew how to bake a *koek*. So did every English mom. But the English word was "cake." Every Dutch mom also knew how to bake a *koekje*—a little cake. I guess people in early America must have thought *koekje* sounded like "koekie," because that's how they eventually said it.

Now, you'll probably say that a little cake is not a cookie; it's a cupcake. And you'll be right. But early Americans used the word *koekie* (cookie) anyway and made cookies like the ones we have today (or wish we had).

I guess the Dutch people who stayed back in the Old Country never caught on. In Holland today, the word "cookie" means cupcake. That makes sense if you know the meaning of the original Dutch word. But please don't make that kind of sense if I ask you for a chocolate chip cookie.

What I want is a round, flat thing that tastes better than almost anything else in the world—especially if it's straight out of the freezer.

VILLAIN

No, I am not.

A villain, as you know, is a no-good character lurking in the shadows, probably waiting for a chance to steal your chocolate chip cookies. Even though I could use one of those cookies right now, I am not a villain.

If you look at the fine print at the beginning of this book, you will see that my poignant, precise, precious, and priceless Professor paragraphs are prepared, produced, and published in Asheville. That could lead you mistakenly to believe that I am somehow up to no good.

Please let me explain.

You see, the "–ville" in Asheville (the same "–ville" that is in Louisville, Greenville, Knoxville, Charlottesville, Nashville, and all the other villes) goes back to the old French word *ville* which means "town." Nothing villainous about that, right? Wrong.

That French word came from the ancient Latin word *villa*, which meant country house or farm. Asheville, as you can see, is a perfectly upstanding name.

The possible confusion with cookie thieves comes from the fact that the Latin word *villa*—and its sister word *villanus* (farm worker)—also led to some not-so-upstanding words. About a thousand years ago, *villanus* became *villein* in French and "villain" in English. They both simply meant "farm worker."

But as things sometimes happen, the meaning of "farm worker" eventually shifted to "clod" which eventually shifted to "low-life" which eventually shifted to "dirtbag," and so on. Today, a villain is an evil person—the bad guy in the story.

So please remember: Although I love to work on the farm and my columns are published in Asheville, I will not steal your chocolate chip cookies.

I may occasionally take a little bite when no one is looking. But that's it.

NORM BOMER

You could easily think that the author of this book is a normal person. It would make sense to conclude that "Norm" comes from the ancient Latin word *normalis*, which meant "made from a pattern" or "made according to a carpenter's square."

Our modern English word "normal" does indeed come from *normalis*, which came from the even older Latin word *normal*, which meant "pattern or rule." These days, "normal" means "fitting with accepted rules." And the "norm" of something is "the standard or rule."

It's probably obvious to you by now that the "Norm" in "Norm Bomer" must come from somewhere else. After all, who would call Norm Bomer normal?

The name "Norm" actually comes from an old Scandinavian word which meant "man from the north." Remember the Norman Invasion, when Scandinavians conquered England in 1066? Those guys came from the north, as did their Viking ancestors.

"Bomer," on the other hand, came from Germany, a little further south. It was originally *baum*, meaning "tree." So I guess Mr. Bomer could be a not-so-normal tree from the north, except that he's sometimes out of his tree.

If all this doesn't scare you too much, you might want to have a look at another of Norm Bomer's books: *Sons of the River—A Nebraska Memoir.* It's about a river and not a tree—and about the struggles of normal people. The author does know something about such folks.

RICH BISHOP

The illustrator of this book is not a rich bishop. He is a Rich Bishop. Confusing?

Let's see if we can straighten this out.

Mr. Bishop probably can't help us get things straight. He's an artist. His lines are whimsical and artsy and looping and curving all over the place. We'll have to find out for ourselves just where that name comes from. Our modern word "rich," as you know, means "wealthy." It goes back about 1500 years to the Old English word *rice*, which meant both "powerful and wealthy." Obviously something is wrong here. Rich Bishop is just a regular guy.

Here's what's wrong: His name has nothing to do with being rich. It has to do with being Richard. And like "Norm" it comes from the Normans. "Richard" was one of their most popular names, derived from the really old German words *rik* (king) and *harthu* (hard).

Does that mean Mr. Bishop is a hard old king? No. I already told you— he's not even a bishop. A prince maybe. A soft one.

In England—long before the 1066 Norman Invasion, the "Bishop" family name did indeed come from "bishop," meaning "church elder or overseer." But our Mr. Bishop's more recent ancestors were Dutch like he is. They had fled to Holland centuries ago seeking religious freedom.

And it's a good thing for you that they did. Otherwise, this book might not have such cool illustrations. That's a poor thought, not a rich one.

Now there are even more reasons to subscribe to *God's World News*.

"Current Events Timely."

The reporting in every issue of **God's World News** is timely, but the biblical perspective is timeless. Engagingly written and designed, **God's World News** will help you:

- Show your children the variety, beauty, and wonder of God's world
- Weave current events into your homeschool curriculum
- Prepare your children to contend with viewpoints at odds with Christian values

A complete, better-than-ever package

God's World News includes 26 weeks of news (September to May) tailored to four reading levels, plus educational posters, maps, puzzles, games, weekly teaching aids, resources on gwnews.com, and many enjoyable new additions.

Combine orders and SAVE! Call 800-951-5437 for details.

Each paid subscription includes:

26 Weekly Issues (Sept. - May) Receive current news and activities that help your child understand world events from a Christian worldview.

Free Teacher's Helpers These weekly guides help you use the papers to build kids' critical thinking skills and reading comprehension.

As many as 8 FREE educational posters, including a world map Use these colorful, instructive posters as curriculum supplements or as educational art for your children's room!

Other Publications You can introduce your children to **God's World News** and keep them reading and learning happily all through the summer.

You'll receive three monthly, 16-page issues of **SUMMER TIMES**.

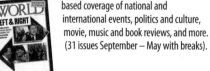

For your high schoolers, there's **WORLD Magazine**, with interesting biblically-based coverage of national and international events, politics and culture, movie, music and book reviews, and more. (31 issues September – May with breaks).